National Sailing Scheme

Syllabus & Logbook

© RYA

Fourth Edition 2019

Reprinted June 2019

The Royal Yachting Association

RYA House, Ensign Way,

Hamble, Southampton,

Hampshire SO31 4YA

Tel: 02380 604 100

Web: www.rya.org.uk

Follow us on Twitter @RYAPublications or on YouTube

We welcome feedback on our publications at publications@rya.org.uk

You can check content updates for RYA publications at www.rya.org.uk/go/bookschangelog

ISBN 978-1-910017272

RYA Order Code G4

Sustainable
Forests

EMAS
VERIFIED
ENVIRONMENTAL
MANAGEMENT

A CIP record of this book is available from the British Library

Note: While all reasonable care has been taken in the preparation of this book, the publisher takes no responsibility for the use of the methods or products or contracts described in this book.

Cover design: Jude Williams

Photographic credits: Karen Bornhoft, Harry Bowerman, David Eberlin, Paul Hargreaves, Jon Holt, Malcolm Lewin, Minorca Sailing, Sportography.tv, Rick Tomlinson, Emily Whiting, Paul Wyeth.

Typeset: Jude Williams

Proofreading: Matthew Gale

Printed in China through World Print

CONTENTS

Photo credit: Paul Wyeth

INTRODUCTION

Sailing is a fantastic and diverse sport, with activities to suit everyone. The RYA National Sailing Scheme has been designed to help you enjoy whichever aspect of the sport appeals to you. All the courses in the Scheme can be taken in a dinghy, keelboat, or multihull so you can have tuition in whatever type of boat you wish.

Good sailing!

Amanda Van Santen
RYA Chief Instructor, Dinghy & Windsurfing

THE RYA NATIONAL SAILING SCHEME MODEL

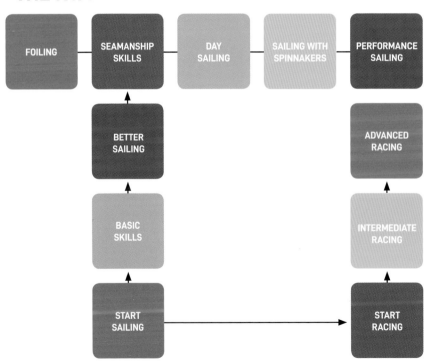

THE RYA NATIONAL SAILING SCHEME

How to Find the Right Sailing Course

The reputation of the RYA National Sailing Scheme has been built on high standards and good tuition. RYA Training Centres vary according to the sailing area available and the type of boats and level of tuition on offer. Whether you wish to learn to sail locally or improve your sailing on holiday, there should be an RYA Training Centre to suit you. To select a course that will meet your needs, visit the RYA website (www.rya.org.uk/wheresmynearest) for a list of sailing schools near you.

Some RYA Training Centres have specialised facilities (including boats) for people with disabilities. Others can offer integrated courses in standard boats. Some students with disabilities may need additional help to complete the full requirements for an RYA certificate.

There is provision within the Scheme for certificates to be endorsed as appropriate. Please contact the Principal of your selected RYA Training Centre or the RYA for more information.

What is an RYA Recognised Training Centre?

Safety is a priority for the RYA. Each RYA Training Centre is regularly inspected for standards of tuition, facilities, and equipment, as laid down by RYA Training and published in the guidance notes. All must have qualified staff, suitable boats, and adequate safety cover. RYA Training Centres should display a Certificate of Recognition specifying the activities for which they are recognised. They are also required to carry public liability insurance.

For Beginners' courses run in single-handed dinghies, there should be an Instructor to a maximum of six students in single-handed dinghies, or one to three in crewed dinghies with the Instructor on board. Keelboat courses can be run with an Instructor/student ratio of up to one to four.

Training carried out in coastal conditions that are not tidal should include the tidal material in the relevant sections.

At the end of your course, the Principal or Chief Instructor will decide whether certificates are to be awarded. Certificates are specific to the type of boat used, i.e. dinghy, keelboat, or multihull. If the Principal decides that further practice is necessary before awarding you a certificate, they will explain the reasons to you. Should you feel it necessary to appeal against the outcome, contact RYA Training for guidance.

The Courses

All the courses in the RYA National Sailing Scheme can be spread over a series of sessions covering a period of 16 hours or in just two days. Most are flexible and often available as evening or half-day sessions too.

Direct Assessments

Experienced sailors may wish to have direct assessment of their skills rather than taking part in a training course. The criteria are outlined in this book. Individual items will be signed off by the assessing Instructor and the declaration signed by the Principal or Chief Instructor.

Photo credit: David Eberlin

What Next?

After taking your course you may consider joining a club, or buying a boat and joining the class association, who organise a variety of events. The RYA website (www.rya.org.uk) is a good place to find a club or locate your class association.

How to Become an Instructor

Having learnt to sail, you may enjoy passing your skills on to others. The RYA Instructor is an experienced sailor who has successfully completed a sailing test (the pre-entry test) and an Instructor training course. Further information is on the RYA website and pages 36–37. RYA Instructors should also hold a first aid certificate and the RYA Powerboat Level 2 Certificate. Full details are contained in RYA publication G14, RYA National Sailing Scheme Instructor Handbook.

Courses for Young People

The RYA also offers a training scheme for young people, the Youth Sailing Scheme. Full details are published in RYA book G11. Following completion of the Youth Sailing Scheme, young people may participate in further training through the advanced modules of the National Sailing Scheme.

Windsurfing, Powerboating, Sail and Power Cruising

The RYA organises similar training schemes for all these activities. Full details are available from the website or the RYA Training Department.

Learning Resources

The RYA produces a wide range of materials to help you learn, from handbooks to online courses. These can be obtained through RYA Training Centres and the RYA website.

Photo credit: Paul Wyeth

THE DUKE OF EDINBURGH'S AWARD

Are you aged between 14 and 24 and fancy challenging yourself?

The RYA is recognised as a National Operating Authority for The Duke of Edinburgh's Award (DofE). The DofE is a voluntary, non-competitive programme of activities for anyone aged 14 to 24, providing a fantastic opportunity to experience new activities or develop existing skills.

There are three progressive levels of programmes that, when successfully completed, lead to a Bronze, Silver, or Gold Award.

Sailing as part of your DofE

Achieving a DofE Award can be made an adventure from beginning to end. Within an RYA club or training centre there are already many activities you could take part in that can count towards your DofE. These could range from:

Volunteering

Helping out at your local training centre, club, or Team15 night on a regular basis. This could be as an assistant, in the kitchen, or maybe even on the committee!

Physical

Regularly taking part in sailing or windsurfing activity? Why not set yourself a goal to gain a certain certificate in the RYA National Sailing or Windsurfing Schemes, or maybe participate in regular club racing?

Skill

Develop your skills, whether practical, social, or personal. You may choose to sharpen up your powerboating, learn a new skill such as boat repair work, become an Instructor, or perhaps increase your theory knowledge and learn all about meteorology!

Residential and Expedition

You may never have been away from home before, let alone used your board or boat to go on an exciting adventure with friends, so now is the time!

Further information can be found, explaining the opportunities available, on the DofE website (www.dofe.org), and the RYA website (www.rya.org.uk/go/dofe).

LEVEL 1 – START SAILING

This course provides a short introduction to sailing for novices. By the end of the course you will have a basic understanding of dinghy-handling techniques and background knowledge. It is recommended that all participants consolidate this short introduction with the Basic Skills and Better Sailing courses.

Duration: Approximately 16 hours (either spread over a series of sessions or two full days).

Practical

Has a practical understanding of:

RIGGING

Basic rigging, parts of the sail, sail controls and foils ☐

Has wind awareness ashore ☐

SAILING TECHNIQUES AND MANOEUVRES

Wind awareness afloat ☐

Reaching – sailing across the wind ☐

Stopping – Lying-to ☐

Controlling speed ☐

Getting out of irons ☐

Tacking – turning the front of the boat through the wind ☐

Sailing upwind ☐

The Five Essentials ☐

Sailing downwind ☐

Gybing – turning the back of the boat through the wind, from a training run ☐

The importance of good communication when manoeuvring (double-handers) ☐

Can perform a basic capsize recovery, and understands the importance of staying with the boat* (Optional) ☐

*Not necessarily applicable to keelboats

LAUNCHING AND RECOVERY*

Can:

Secure a boat on the trolley ☐

Understands the principles of:

Wheeling a trolley clear of other boats and overhead cables ☐

Launching and leaving the shore ☐

Coming ashore and recovery of a boat ☐

ROPEWORK

Can tie a figure of eight knot, round turn and two half hitches, and secure a rope to a cleat ☐

Sailing Theory

Has theoretical understanding of:

CLOTHING AND EQUIPMENT

Knows the importance of personal safety, clothing, and buoyancy ☐

SAILING BACKGROUND

An awareness of other water users ☐

Basic rules of the road – avoid a collision at all costs, power/sail, port/starboard, overtaking boat, windward boat ☐

Visual methods of attracting attention ☐

METEOROLOGY

Has an awareness of onshore and offshore winds ☐

Sources of weather information and their relevance:

Effects on sailing location ☐

Beaufort Scale ☐

Conditions appropriate to ability and sailing location ☐

Keelboat Sailors

CLOTHING AND EQUIPMENT

Understands:

Use of, and correct fitting of lifejackets ☐

Use of a safety harness if fitted ☐

Man-overboard recovery ☐

MAN OVERBOARD RECOVERY

Understands:

Actions to be taken to recover a man overboard ☐

Use of mooring lines ☐

Emergency equipment and precautions ☐

EMERGENCY EQUIPMENT AND PRECAUTIONS

Has knowledge and awareness of:

Potential hazards and risks of on-board fuel ☐

Stowage and use of fire extinguishers ☐

OTHER ASPECTS

Basic Skills Course ☐

Chief Instructor's/Principal's Signature

RYA Training Centre

Photo credit: Emily Whiting

LEVEL 2 – BASIC SKILLS

On completion of this course, you will have a basic knowledge of sailing and sailing in light winds without an instructor on board. It will be assumed that every student starting this course has already mastered the practical skills and absorbed the background knowledge required for Start Sailing. Both courses can be combined. Dinghy or multihull capsize recovery will be conducted in a controlled manner, one boat at a time, with a suitable rescue boat in attendance.

Duration: Approximately 16 hours (either spread over a series of sessions or two full days).

Practical

Has a practical understanding of:

RIGGING

How to rig according to weather conditions ☐

Reefing ashore* ☐

SAILING TECHNIQUES AND MANOEUVRES

Leaving and returning to a beach, jetty, or mooring ☐

Coming alongside a moored boat ☐

Sailing in close company ☐

Performing a man-overboard recovery ☐

Is aware of lee-shore dangers ☐

The Five Essentials ☐

Can tack while sailing upwind, showing refined skill, losing minimal ground ☐

Can gybe in a controlled manner while sailing downwind ☐

Shows good communication when manoeuvring (double-handers) ☐

Understands and shows awareness of other water users ☐

Can sail around a short course using all points of sail and crewing skills ☐

ROPEWORK

Can tie a bowline, clove hitch, and reef knot ☐

CAPSIZE RECOVERY

Can right a capsized boat using one method of righting, and has knowledge of at least one other ☐

RACING

Understands the course and starting procedure (may be covered as onshore teaching) ☐

BASIC ADVICE FOR INDEPENDENT SAILING:

Self-reliance and basic equipment ☐

Visual methods of attracting attention ☐

Has knowledge of:

The points of sailing and the 'No-go Zone' ☐

How a sail works ☐

How a sailing boat moves (basic theory) ☐

*Not necessarily applicable to keelboats

METEOROLOGY

Has knowledge of:

Sources of relevant weather, inshore forecasts, and their interpretation ☐

The Beaufort Wind Scale ☐

When to reef ☐

How to understand a simple synoptic chart ☐

Keelboat Sailors

RIGGING

Can reef afloat ☐

ROPEWORK

Can use winches ☐

USE OF ENGINES (IF FITTED)

Has knowledge of engine checks, starting, stopping, and running procedures ☐

Can come alongside and pick up a mooring ☐

SAILING TECHNIQUES AND MANOEUVRES

Can:

Anchor ☐

Sail using transits ☐

EMERGENCY EQUIPMENT AND PRECAUTIONS

Knows the importance of first aid kits and flares, including stowage ☐

Multihull Sailors

SAILING TECHNIQUES AND MANOEUVRES

Understands the basic principles of crew weight, airflow, technique (CAT) ☐

SAILING THEORY

Has theoretical understanding of: ☐

CLOTHING AND EQUIPMENT

Knows the importance of personal safety, clothing, basic personal and boat buoyancy ☐

LAUNCHING AND RECOVERY

Boat storage ashore, launching, and recovery ☐

SAILING BACKGROUND

Has knowledge of:

Basic rules of the road; avoid collisions at all costs, power/sail, port/starboard, windward boat, overtaking boat ☐

Coastal Waters

Can apply the practical section in coastal waters ☐

Understands:

How to apply weather forecasts in coastal waters ☐

Tide tables, tidal sequence of springs and neaps, ebb and flow ☐

Speed over ground with/against tidal flow ☐

The effect of wind direction and tidal flow on sailing conditions ☐

The importance of informing someone ashore, and the dangers of sailing alone ☐

How to access local information and advice for sea sailing ☐

OTHER ASPECTS

Better Sailing Course ☐

Opportunities for regular activity (local club and centre activity and groups, etc.) ☐

Purchasing your own equipment ☐

Basic racing ☐

Chief Instructor's/Principal's Signature

RYA Training Centre

LEVEL 3 – BETTER SAILING

This improver course seeks to bridge the gap between Start Sailing, Basic Skills, and the Advanced modules by offering an introduction to the different modules, allowing sailors to select more easily their preferred route within the sport. Better Sailing allows for opportunity to practise and consolidate sailing techniques, and experience some of the activities the Advanced modules have to offer, helping to build confidence and support development of good technique and independent sailing.

Additional module options are non-compulsory for completion of the Better Sailing course, but are designed to provide an introduction to the various aspects of sailing. Which elements are chosen should be discussed by student and Instructor. Where practicable, students should be provided with the opportunity to sail different dinghies during the course, single and double-handers.

Duration: Approximately 16 hours (either spread over a series of sessions or two full days).

Practical

Has a practical understanding of:

SAILING TECHNIQUES AND MANOEUVRES

Understands how to use rig and sail controls to prepare the boat according to different weather conditions and sea states ☐

Can check a spinnaker is rigged correctly (if fitted) ☐

CORE SKILLS

Can:

Leave and return to a shore, jetty, or mooring (including windward and leeward shore in light conditions) ☐

Recover a man overboard effectively ☐

Use the sail tell-tales effectively ☐

Reef a sail when required ☐

Demonstrate a 'dry capsize' ☐

Understand how to avoid inversion ☐

Sail using efficient and skilful application of the Five Essentials ☐

Tack – maintaining boat speed and balance, upwind ☐

Gybe – maintaining boat speed and balance ☐

Show good use of crew and to best effect (where applicable) ☐

Understand when, and the importance of, timing manoeuvres ☐

Sailing Background

Has theoretical understanding of:

The IRPCS, and can apply them to:

Other sailing vessels ☐

Power-driven vessels ☐

Following or crossing narrow channels ☐

Action by stand-on vessel ☐

Basic sail-control knowledge to change the sail shape and power ☐

Understands:

The points of sailing ☐

The Five Essentials ☐

Basic meteorology terminology, including the Beaufort Scale ☐

How to obtain a weather forecast ☐

How to interpret a basic synoptic chart ☐

Awareness of changing weather conditions ☐

Additional Module Options:

Has both practical and theoretical understanding of the following:

SEAMANSHIP SKILLS

Can demonstrate anchoring in various conditions ☐

Introduction to sailing in adverse conditions (centreboardless, rudderless sailing) ☐

RACE SKILLS

Has knowledge of the 'simplified World Sailing Racing Rules of Sailing' ☐

Can:

Start and finish a simple race ☐

Choose the best route to sail around a course, depending on conditions (using the Five Essentials) ☐

DAY SAILING SKILLS

Basic chart orientation – including cardinal and lateral buoyage systems ☐

Can take bearings and measure distances on a chart ☐

Understands the effect of tide and wind direction on sailing conditions ☐

Can:

Use a local tide table ☐

Follow a pre-planned route ☐

SPINNAKER SAILING SKILLS

Basic introduction to spinnaker handling as crew or helm, including rig, hoist, and drop ☐

PERFORMANCE SAILING SKILLS

Basic introduction to trapezing with Instructor on the helm (Optional – boat-dependant) ☐

Introduction to better hiking technique ☐

OTHER ASPECTS

The Advanced modules ☐

Opportunities to sail regularly ☐

Introduction to high-performance boats ☐

Local club racing ☐

Chief Instructor's/Principal's Signature

RYA Training Centre

Photo credit: Malcolm Lewin

15

SEAMANSHIP SKILLS

On successful completion of this course, you will be capable of manoeuvring a dinghy/keelboat/multihull in a seamanlike manner and making seamanship decisions in moderate conditions.

It will be assumed that, when starting on this course, you have already mastered the practical skills and absorbed the background knowledge required for the previous levels.

Tuition will be given by trained Instructors, using appropriate supervision ratios with regard to the location and competence of the students. Much of the work afloat will be done without an Instructor aboard. The emphasis is on increasing the self-reliance and decision-making of the sailor.

Duration: Approximately 16 hours (either spread over a series of sessions or two full days).

Practical

ROPEWORK

Can tie a fisherman's bend, rolling hitch, and sheet bend ☐

LAUNCHING AND RECOVERY

Can leave and return to beach, jetty, or mooring, including windward and leeward shore ☐

Sailing techniques and manoeuvres ☐

Can:

Heave to ☐

Reef afloat ☐

Recover a man overboard ☐

Be towed by a power vessel ☐

Anchor, including understanding principles and techniques for different circumstances† ☐

Sail backwards ☐

Sail in adverse circumstances (no rudder, no centreboard)*† ☐

Prepare a road trailer and secure a boat for transportation (optional) ☐

Sailing Background

SAILING THEORY AND BACKGROUND

Understands the following terminology:

Windward, leeward, abeam, forward, aft, ahead, astern, to weather, downwind, amidships, quarter, pinching, sailing by the lee, luff, bear away, planing, sternway, broaching ☐

Knows and can apply the following International Regulations for the Prevention of Collisions at Sea (IRPCS):

Meeting other sailing vessels, meeting power-driven vessels, following or crossing narrow channels, action by stand-on vessel ☐

CAPSIZE RECOVERY

Knows how to recover from total inversion (practical session if possible) ☐

METEOROLOGY

Knows sources of information on weather patterns for the day ☐

*Not necessarily applicable to keelboats
†Not necessarily applicable to multihulls

Can interpret forecasts and understand local effects ☐

Is aware of Beaufort Wind Scale and changing weather conditions, including fog ☐

COASTAL (OPTIONAL)

Capable of practical application of Section A on coastal waters ☐

Can use local tide tables ☐

Understands rate of rise and fall – Twelfths Rule ☐

Is aware of tidal streams ☐

Has a basic understanding of charts and important symbols ☐

Experienced Sailor's Direct Assessment

The candidate should be able to demonstrate satisfactorily aspects of practical and theory knowledge, afloat and ashore, answering any questions. Candidates seeking assessment on coastal waters will demonstrate knowledge from the coastal section option. ☐

———————————————————
Chief Instructor's/Principal's Signature

———————————————————
RYA Training Centre

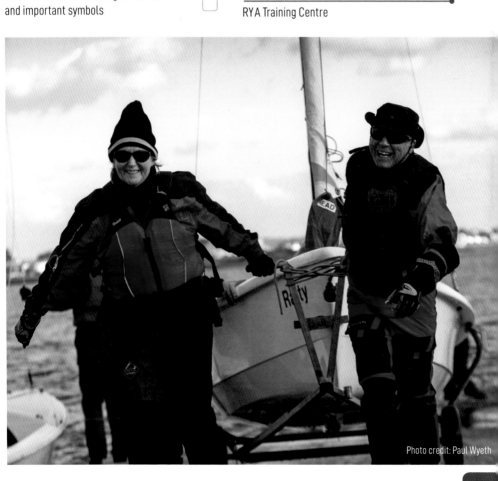

Photo credit: Paul Wyeth

DAY SAILING

The course will include the planning and execution of a day sail, and, on successful completion, you will have a confident, safe approach to planning and executing a short day sail in a dinghy/keelboat/multihull.

On starting this course you should have already mastered the practical skills and absorbed the background knowledge required for the previous levels. In addition, sailors wishing to cruise independently should ensure that they understand and can carry out the manoeuvres in the Seamanship Skills (see page 16) part of the RYA National Sailing Scheme.

Candidates who hold the RYA Essential Navigation & Seamanship course completion certificate or a higher-level RYA cruising award may gain exemption from necessary chartwork.

Duration: Approximately 16 hours (either spread over a series of sessions or two full days).

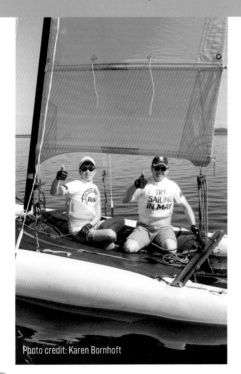

Photo credit: Karen Bornhoft

Practical

RIGGING

Can prepare and equip a boat for cruising, including safety and navigation equipment, clothing and food, and stow gear correctly ☐

SAILING TECHNIQUES AND MANOEUVRES

Can plan and undertake a day sail including a consideration of pilotage/navigation and collision avoidance ☐

Can use the anchor to effect lee-shore landing and departure*† ☐

ADVERSE CONDITIONS

Is able to self-rescue following total inversion* ☐

Understands how to improvise in the event of gear failure ☐

*Not necessarily applicable to keelboats
†Not necessarily applicable to multihulls

Sailing Background

SAILING THEORY AND BACKGROUND

Has knowledge of boat handling in strong winds and difficult conditions (practical where possible) ☐

NAVIGATION

Can plan a day's cruise in coastal waters, including knowledge of:

Publications available, particularly charts, tide tables, tidal stream atlases ☐

Navigational instruments and their limitations afloat ☐

Use of GPS, including waypoint navigation ☐

Confirming position by another source ☐

Tidal heights and tidal streams (Rule of Twelfths or percentage rule), probable changes in the weather, and the interaction of weather and tidal streams ☐

Decision-making in adverse circumstances, including planning alternatives and refuges ☐

Magnetic compass: variation and deviation ☐

Interpretation of charts ☐

Use of transits and bearings to steer course and fix position ☐

Recording position and principles of dead reckoning ☐

METEOROLOGY

Knows sources of information on weather patterns for the day ☐

Understands main characteristics of high- and low-pressure systems and simple interpretation of synoptic charts ☐

Has awareness of changing weather conditions ☐

Experienced Sailor's Direct Assessment

The candidate should be able to demonstrate satisfactorily competence in areas of both practical and background knowledge, ashore and afloat. ☐

_____

Chief Instructor's/Principal's Signature

_____

RYA Training Centre

Photo credit: Jon Holt

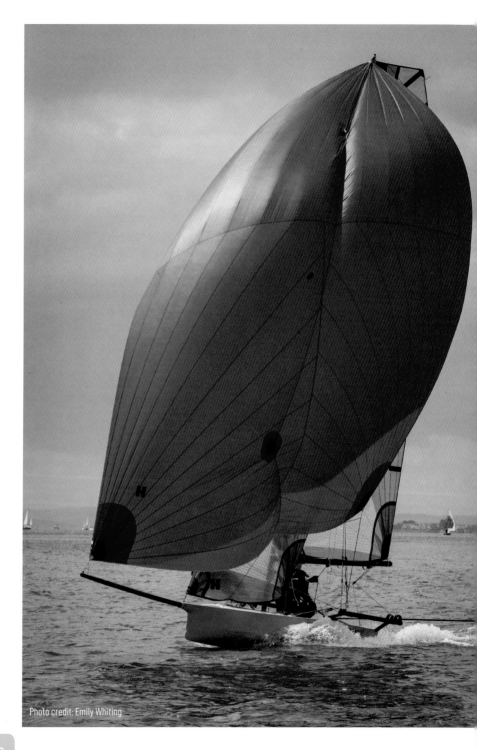

Photo credit: Emily Whiting

SAILING WITH SPINNAKERS

On successful completion of this course you will understand how to sail a dinghy/keelboat/multihull rigged with an asymmetric or symmetric spinnaker. It is assumed when starting this course you have already mastered the practical skills and absorbed the background knowledge required for previous levels. Tuition will be given by an Advanced Instructor, or by an Instructor with appropriate experience approved by the Principal, using appropriate supervision ratios with regard to the location and competence of the students.

Duration: Approximately 16 hours (either spread over a series of sessions or two full days).

Practical

RIGGING

Can rig boats, including spinnaker, and trapeze where fitted ☐

LAUNCHING AND RECOVERY

Understands how to launch boats with open transoms and/or racks*† ☐

SAILING TECHNIQUES AND MANOEUVRES

Can sail as crew or helm using equipment to good advantage ☐

Can perform spinnaker hoist, gybe, and drop as crew or helm ☐

Understands and can sail best course downwind ☐

CAPSIZE RECOVERY

Can perform capsize recovery including spinnaker ☐

Knows how to recover from total inversion* ☐

Sailing Background

RACING

Has knowledge of courses for type of boat ☐

SAILING THEORY AND BACKGROUND

Understands the concept of apparent wind sailing ☐

Understands the effect of hull shape on performance ☐

Can access sources of information and apply rig set-up for different conditions ☐

Experienced Sailor's Direct Assessment

Candidates should be able to demonstrate satisfactorily competence and confidence in areas afloat and ashore, practical and of sailing background. ☐

_____

Chief Instructor's/Principal's Signature

_____

RYA Training Centre

*Not necessarily applicable to keelboats
†Not necessarily applicable to multihulls

PERFORMANCE SAILING

On successful completion of this course, you will understand how to sail performance dinghies/keelboats/multihulls in all wind conditions that you can expect to encounter, sailing the boat to best advantage at all times.

The emphasis is on coaching to improve your sailing performance and will therefore involve coaching from powerboats. This course is intended primarily for two-person spinnaker boats; however, it may be delivered in performance single-handers and the certificate endorsed accordingly.

Tuition will be given by an Advanced Instructor for the type of boat, using appropriate supervision ratios with regard to the location and competence of the students, and the need to provide continuous feedback on the water. It is assumed that every student starting this course has already mastered the practical skills and absorbed the background knowledge required for previous levels. In practical terms, at least a full season's sailing experience since learning to sail is advisable.

Duration: Approximately 16 hours (either spread over a series of sessions or two full days).

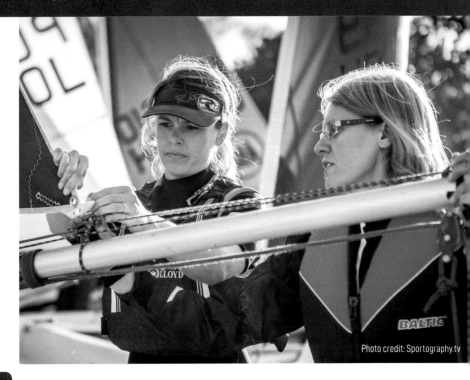

Photo credit: Sportography.tv

Practical

RIGGING

Can rig any type of boat, including
spinnaker and trapeze (if fitted) ☐

Understands basic rig setup and tuning ☐

SAILING TECHNIQUES
AND MANOEUVRES

Can make best possible use of crew and
equipment to sail efficiently on all points
of sailing in a variety of conditions, including ☐
symmetric or asymmetric spinnaker

Can use sail controls to effect changes
to shape and power of sails ☐

Can spot and use wind shifts and gusts to
effect best course up and down wind ☐

Can perform capsize recovery including
spinnaker. Knows how to recover from ☐
total inversion*

Can tack, refining skills according
to conditions ☐

Shows understanding of roll-tacking
principles ☐

Can gybe, refining skills according
to conditions ☐

Shows understanding of roll-gybing
principles ☐

Sailing Background

SAILING THEORY AND BACKGROUND

Understands how to make use of wind
variation and tidal eddies which occur due ☐
to geographical features and tidal conditions

Has an understanding of hull shapes and rig
types, including their effect on performance ☐

Understands planing and the effect of rails ☐

*Not necessarily applicable to keelboats

METEOROLOGY

Knows sources of information on
weather patterns for the day ☐

Understands main characteristics of
high- and low-pressure systems, ☐
and simple interpretation of synoptic charts

Has awareness of changing
weather conditions ☐

EXPERIENCED SAILOR'S
DIRECT ASSESSMENT

Candidates should show confidence and
competence in practical and sailing ☐
background areas, both afloat and ashore.

Chief Instructor's/Principal's Signature

RYA Training Centre

Photo credit: Paul Wyeth

RYA SAILFOILING COURSES: FIRST FLIGHTS

This first session in SAILfoiling provides an initial introduction into the amazing and exhilarating world of foiling. As a pre-requisite, you should hold the RYA Level 2 Basic Skills, which will ensure you have the necessary skills to take on foiling!

Aimed as a taster session, First Flights provides you with a basic introduction to foiling, assisting you to make your first foiling take-offs.

Suggested course length: Two to four hours (taster session).

Practical

RIGGING

Has knowledge of:

Assembling and setting up the main foil, rudder, and rudder foil ☐

Various foiling boats ☐

The options and adaptions available for non-foiling boats ☐

Launching and Recovery

Has knowledge of the different launch/recovery methods for different boat designs ☐

SAILING TECHNIQUES AND MANOEUVRES

Can:

Engage and disengage foils ☐

Change course sailed, and adjust sail trim to encourage flight ☐

Take off ☐

Understands and has knowledge of:

How to land safely ☐

How to maintain foiling ☐

Capsize recovery methods ☐

Apparent wind, showing a basic application and sail adjustment ☐

FOILING KNOWLEDGE

Understands and has knowledge of:

The basic theory of how foils work ☐

A range of different foiling boats ☐

Sail adjustments, and how to trim sails ☐

SAFETY

Understands and has knowledge of:

The risks of foiling alone ☐

The lack of noise when approaching other craft ☐

Different personal safety equipment ☐

The importance of foiling in suitable sailing conditions ☐

Chief Instructor's/Principal's Signature

RYA Training Centre

edit: Paul Wyeth

SUSTAINED FLIGHTS

Sustained Flights is designed to increase your foil handling and control. Having completed this course, you will start to feel more confident about the practical techniques and theory required to foil, steer, and maintain a course effectively. All tacking or gybing at this level is non-foiling.

It will be assumed that every student starting this course has already mastered the practical skills and absorbed the background knowledge required for First Flights.

Suggested course length: Up to 16 hours, either spread over a series of sessions or full days.

Photo credit: Paul Wyeth

Practical

RIGGING

Can assemble and set up the main foil (with assistance) ☐

Can assemble and set up the rudder and rudder foil (with assistance) ☐

Has knowledge of how to adjust foils in different conditions to optimise performance ☐

Understands how to trim the main foil to adjust the 'ride height' ☐

LAUNCHING AND RECOVERY

Can:

Launch the boat off a slipway/beach using a method specific for that foiling boat (with assistance) ☐

Safely return to slipway/beach using a method specific to that foiling boat ☐

SAILING TECHNIQUE AND MANOEUVRES

Can:

Maintain periods of sustained foiling ☐

Trim sails effectively according to the apparent wind ☐

Demonstrate a non-foiling tack ☐

Demonstrate a non-foiling gybe ☐

Adjust bow height and trim through the rudder foil ☐

Show basic skills and understanding of foiling on various points of sail ☐

FOILING KNOWLEDGE

Technique:

Understands the apparent-wind effect and how to trim effectively according to the point of sail ☐

Understands different ride heights and how to adjust the main foil to enable the boat to ride higher or lower ☐

Has knowledge of correct angles for tack entry and exit ☐

Has knowledge of correct angles for gybe entry and exit ☐

Theory

Understands:

How the wand works ☐

How twist tillers adjust the rudder ☐

Righting moment and how it is achieved ☐

SAFETY

Has knowledge of safety equipment which may be worn while foiling ☐

_____•

Chief Instructor's/Principal's Signature

_____•

RYA Training Centre

Photo credit: Paul Wyeth

PERFORMANCE FLIGHTS

Performance Flights is the last of the RYA foiling courses, looking at advanced skills and technique. This course will increase your confidence on different angles, while also looking at entry and exit into manoeuvres, providing you with a good understanding as to the theory.

It will be assumed that every student starting this course has the knowledge and practical ability of RYA Sustained Flights or above.

Suggested course length: Up to 16 hours, either spread over a series of sessions or full days.

Practical

SAILING TECHNIQUE AND MANOEUVRES

Can:

Demonstrate foiling upwind and downwind ☐

Effectively set up, balance, and steer into the tack ☐

Demonstrate tack entry while foiling, exiting in control ☐

Can:

Effectively set up, balance, and steer into the gybe ☐

Demonstrate gybe entry while foiling, exiting in control ☐

FOILING KNOWLEDGE

Can:

Steer and adopt the correct body movements required to foil through a gybe ☐

Adjust wand settings and ride height for optimum performance in different conditions ☐

Understands:

The theory and technique required to set up and approach the 'entry' of a foiling tack and gybe ☐

The theory and technique required to set up and approach the 'exit' for a foiling tack and gybe ☐

What causes and how to deal with a pitch pole (specific boats) ☐

Different wand systems and what they are used for ☐

SAFETY

Understands the importance of safe sailing areas and suitable sailing conditions to assist with the practise of performance foiling manoeuvres ☐

_____

Chief Instructor's/Principal's Signature

_____

RYA Training Centre

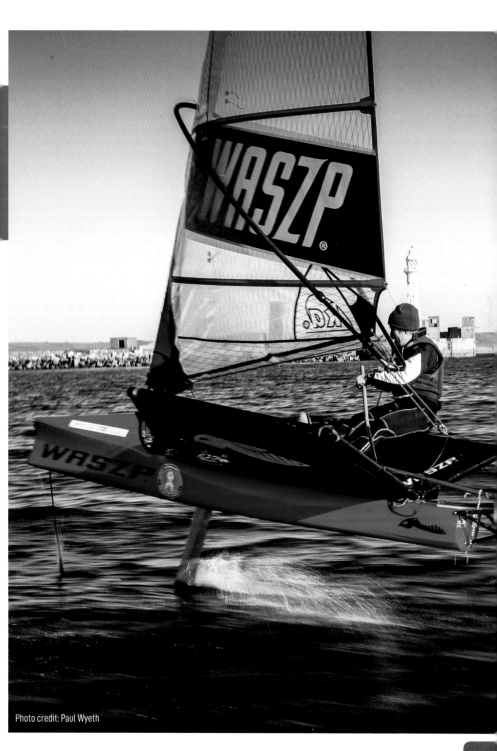

Photo credit: Paul Wyeth

RYA RACING COURSES
START RACING

This course is designed to give the confidence, skills, and knowledge to take part in club racing in good conditions. Confidence is essential if the sailor is to enjoy racing. The course involves the sailor in a range of enjoyable exercises designed to build confidence and improve skills through practice. It is assumed that every student starting this course has already mastered the practical skills and absorbed the background knowledge required for previous levels.

Photo credit: Paul Wyeth

PHYSICAL AND MENTAL PREPARATION

Has knowledge of:

Food as fuel ☐

Keeping hydrated ☐

BOAT PREPARATION

Has knowledge of:

Availability of class tuning guides ☐

Basic tuning ☐

BOAT HANDLING

Has a basic understanding of:

Making best use of the Five
Essentials as helm ☐

Crew (double-handers only) ☐

Mark-rounding ☐

Laylines ☐

Hiking ☐

BOAT SPEED

Understands how to alter sail controls,
both round the course and for
differing conditions ☐

TEAMWORK (FOR DOUBLE-HANDERS)

Understands the requirements to develop
a good partnership ☐

STRATEGY AND METEOROLOGY

Can obtain and understand a simple weather forecast ☐

Has knowledge of clean air, gusts, and lulls ☐

RACING RULES

Has a basic understanding of the Racing Rules of Sailing (Part 2, section A) ☐

Has an understanding of the basic rights of way rules:

Port/starboard (rule 10) ☐

Windward boat (rule 11) ☐

Clear ahead/clear astern (rule 12) ☐

Tacking (rule 13) ☐

TACTICS

Has knowledge of basic boat-on-boat situations ☐

STARTS

Has knowledge of transits ☐

Can demonstrate the basics of starting ☐

OTHER ASPECTS

An introduction to local club racing ☐

Chief Instructor's/Principal's Signature

RYA Training Centre

Photo credit: Paul Hargreaves

INTERMEDIATE RACING

This course builds on the knowledge and skills learnt from 'Start Racing', developing greater awareness of the key principles of starting, boat handling, boat speed, strategy, and tactics, through course time and regular race activity.

PHYSICAL AND MENTAL PREPARATION

Understands the importance of fitness for sailing ☐

BOAT PREPARATION

Has knowledge of:

How to use a tuning guide ☐

How to set a boat up for specific conditions ☐

Understands:
How to prepare a boat for club racing, including:

Hull ☐

Spars ☐

Sails ☐

Foils ☐

Fittings ☐

Rigging ☐

Control lines ☐

BOAT HANDLING

Has knowledge of how to steer the boat without the rudder ☐

Understands the principles involved in:

Slow-speed handling, including: ☐

Stopping ☐

Accelerating ☐

Sailing backwards ☐

Roll tacking ☐

Roll gybing ☐

BOAT SPEED

Has knowledge of basic aerodynamics:

How a sail works ☐

How to power up the rig ☐

How to de-power the rig ☐

Weather helm ☐

Lee helm ☐

How to set up the boat for a range of conditions ☐

TEAMWORK (DOUBLE-HANDERS)

Understands how to divide up the:

Roles around the course ☐

Jobs in the boat ☐

STRATEGY AND METEOROLOGY

Understands:

Clean air ☐

Gusts ☐

Lulls ☐

How to interpret a weather forecast in relation to the sailing venue ☐

RACING RULES

Understands:

Has a good understanding of Part 1, Section A, and the Definitions of the Racing Rules ☐

Basic understanding of Sections B/C/D ☐

Understands how to sail by the Racing Rules ☐

TACTICS

Understands:

Boat-on-boat tactics ☐

Lee bow situation ☐

How to cover and break cover ☐

The importance of clean air ☐

STARTS

Understands bias, and how to assess it ☐

Has knowledge of:

How to hold the boat on the line (hovering) ☐

Accelerating off the line ☐

OTHER ASPECTS

Has knowledge of and participates regularly in club and open meetings ☐

Chief Instructor's/Principal's Signature

RYA Training Centre

Photo credit: Paul Hargreaves

ADVANCED RACING

A predominantly practical course, Advanced Racing is all about developing skills in preparation for open meetings and higher-level competition.

MENTAL AND PHYSICAL PREPARATION

Understands how to, and the value of, goal-setting ☐

BOAT PREPARATION

Understands how to:

Improve foil finish ☐

Optimise boat to class rules ☐

Use a tuning guide ☐

BOAT HANDLING

Understands the principles of:

Steering with sails ☐

Balance ☐

Demonstrating principles in taking penalty turns ☐

Can demonstrate good techniques in a full range of conditions:

Tacking ☐

Gybing ☐

BOAT SPEED

Understands:

The relevance of sail controls and effects on the sail(s) ☐

How to change gears in different conditions while on the water ☐

How to vary the tuning guide for different conditions ☐

How to create your own tuning guide ☐

How to create your own post-race analysis sheet ☐

TEAMWORK (DOUBLE-HANDERS)

Understands effective:

Race analysis ☐

Race and training goals ☐

Can:

Communicate effectively ☐

React to changing circumstances ☐

STRATEGY AND METEOROLOGY

Can create a race strategy prior to going afloat based on weather forecasts and tide tables etc. ☐

RACING RULES

Has good knowledge and understanding of the Racing Rules of Sailing, Part 2 ☐

Understands the RYA Racing Charter ☐

TACTICS

Has knowledge of:

Holding a lane upwind ☐

Boat-on-fleet tactics ☐

Attacking ☐

Controlling situations ☐

Understands:

Boat-on-group tactics ☐

Overtaking and defending tactics ☐

Covering ☐

Different approaches to marks – when to gybe or bear away ☐

STARTS

Understands pre-start rules ☐

Can:

Protect a gap to leeward ☐

Hold the boat on the line (hovering) ☐

Use transits ☐

Has knowledge of:

Various start sequences ☐

Recall signals ☐

Starting penalties ☐

OTHER ASPECTS

Participates regularly in:

Open meetings ☐

National class events ☐

Chief Instructor's/Principal's Signature

RYA Training Centre

Photo credit:Harry Bowerman

Instructor Training

If you have enjoyed your experiences of learning to sail and developing your sailing techniques and skills through the RYA National Sailing Scheme, why not consider sharing your enthusiasm, expertise, and skills with others by becoming involved in the RYA Instructor Training programme?

Below are brief details concerning the basic training courses. More information can be found in G14 RYA National Sailing Scheme Instructor Handbook.

RYA ASSISTANT INSTRUCTOR

Duration: Two days/20 hours

The RYA Assistant Instructor is trained to assist qualified Instructors to teach beginners up to the standard of the RYA National Sailing Scheme Level 2 and the RYA Youth Sailing Scheme Stage 3. They must only work under the supervision of a Senior Instructor. The award is centre-specific.

ELIGIBILITY FOR THE TRAINING COURSE

Pass one of the RYA National Sailing Scheme Advanced Modules or equivalent personal sailing standard. Recommendation by Principal of training centre.

TRAINING

Training will cover the centre's safe-operation procedures and the teaching points related to teaching beginners. The award is centre-specific.

Training is based on a two-day or modular course of 20 hours' duration at the centre run by the Principal/Chief Instructor who holds a valid RYA Senior Instructor certificate.

ASSESSMENT

Candidates will be assessed on their practical teaching ability with beginners. Successful candidates will be awarded an RYA Assistant Instructor certificate by their Principal.

RYA Instructor Pre-Entry Sailing Assessment

The Pre-entry is an essential prerequisite to the RYA Dinghy Instructor course. It is a practical test determining whether a candidate has the required sailing ability, control, and seamanship to become an Instructor. The assessment is conducted by an RYA Coach/Assessor and only valid for one year. During the assessment candidates are judged on their preparation and execution of each task, including awareness of others, and showing confident sailing at all times with awareness of 'the Five Essentials'. During the assessment, the Assessor will be seeking to confirm the candidate can sail in a controlled and competent manner, considering preparation, communication, approach, and execution for each exercise. These may include: sail around a triangular course; sail a tight circular course; sail a follow-my-leader course; pick up a man-overboard dummy, and other skills-based exercises including rudderless, lee-shore landing and departure, pick up mooring or anchor, come alongside a moored boat, and recover a capsized dinghy and sail away. This provides an overall impression of sailing ability and whether it is of the standard required to attend the instructor course.

DINGHY/KEELBOAT/ MULTIHULL/FOILING INSTRUCTOR

Duration: Five days/50 hours.

It is possible to complete the RYA National Sailing Scheme in dinghies, keelboats, or multihulls. Therefore, Instructors teaching the Scheme must be qualified for the type of boat in which they will be teaching. The Instructor certificate will show whether the Instructor is qualified to teach on inland or coastal waters (depending on where they completed the pre-entry sailing assessment and course).

ROLE

Competent, experienced sailor able to sail in strong winds

Can teach RYA National Sailing Scheme up to and including Seamanship Skills, Day Sailing, Sailing with Spinnakers, and RYA Youth Sailing Scheme Stages 1–4

Will only work under the supervision of the RYA Senior Instructor

ELIGIBILITY FOR THE TRAINING COURSE

Minimum age 16

Valid first aid certificate

RYA Powerboat Level 2 certificate

RYA Safe & Fun

Pre-entry sailing assessment completed

RYA membership

TRAINING

- The structure and content of the RYA National Sailing Scheme and RYA Youth Sailing Scheme
- Training in RYA teaching methods, including teaching both adults and children
- Preparation and presentation of a lesson
- Preparation and use of visual aids
- The assessment of students' abilities
- The use of powered craft in a teaching environment

ASSESSMENT

The assessment will be based on an overall (or holistic) judgement throughout the week and during the Instructor moderation day.

This assessment will include:

- Enthusiasm for the sport
- Sailing ability
- Confidence and knowledge in the subject
- Awareness of safety
- Practical teaching according to RYA methods
- Theory knowledge
- Successful demonstrations and clear explanations
- Correct diagnosis and tactful correction of students' faults
- Safe powerboat handling in a teaching environment

Photo credit: Paul Wyeth

PERSONAL LOG

DATE	TYPE OF BOAT	HOURS' EXPERIENCE		ACTIVITY & WEATHER CONDITIONS		AUTHORISATION
		HELM	CREW	TYPE OF COURSE OR ACTIVITY	MAX WIND SPEED	CENTRE/CLUB INSTRUCTOR

PERSONAL LOG

DATE	TYPE OF BOAT	HOURS' EXPERIENCE		ACTIVITY & WEATHER CONDITIONS		AUTHORISATION
		HELM	CREW	TYPE OF COURSE OR ACTIVITY	MAX WIND SPEED	CENTRE/CLUB INSTRUCTOR

COURSE CERTIFICATES

**PLEASE ATTACH YOUR
RYA CERTIFICATE HERE**

Please note that no record of
certificates is held by the RYA

Enquiries about lost certificates
should be made to the centre
where the course was taken

COURSE CERTIFICATES

**PLEASE ATTACH YOUR
RYA CERTIFICATE HERE**

Please note that no record of
certificates is held by the RYA

Enquiries about lost certificates
should be made to the centre
where the course was taken

COURSE CERTIFICATES

**PLEASE ATTACH YOUR
RYA CERTIFICATE HERE**

Please note that no record of
certificates is held by the RYA

Enquiries about lost certificates
should be made to the centre
where the course was taken

COURSE CERTIFICATES

**PLEASE ATTACH YOUR
RYA CERTIFICATE HERE**

Please note that no record of
certificates is held by the RYA

Enquiries about lost certificates
should be made to the centre
where the course was taken

COURSE CERTIFICATES

**PLEASE ATTACH YOUR
RYA CERTIFICATE HERE**

Please note that no record of
certificates is held by the RYA

Enquiries about lost certificates
should be made to the centre
where the course was taken

COURSE CERTIFICATES

**PLEASE ATTACH YOUR
RYA CERTIFICATE HERE**

Please note that no record of
certificates is held by the RYA

Enquiries about lost certificates
should be made to the centre
where the course was taken

COURSE CERTIFICATES

**PLEASE ATTACH YOUR
RYA CERTIFICATE HERE**

Please note that no record of
certificates is held by the RYA

Enquiries about lost certificates
should be made to the centre
where the course was taken

COURSE CERTIFICATES

**PLEASE ATTACH YOUR
RYA CERTIFICATE HERE**

Please note that no record of
certificates is held by the RYA

Enquiries about lost certificates
should be made to the centre
where the course was taken

COURSE CERTIFICATES

**PLEASE ATTACH YOUR
RYA CERTIFICATE HERE**

Please note that no record of
certificates is held by the RYA

Enquiries about lost certificates
should be made to the centre
where the course was taken

COURSE CERTIFICATES

**PLEASE ATTACH YOUR
RYA CERTIFICATE HERE**

Please note that no record of
certificates is held by the RYA

Enquiries about lost certificates
should be made to the centre
where the course was taken

COURSE CERTIFICATES

**PLEASE ATTACH YOUR
RYA CERTIFICATE HERE**

Please note that no record of
certificates is held by the RYA

Enquiries about lost certificates
should be made to the centre
where the course was taken

COURSE CERTIFICATES

**PLEASE ATTACH YOUR
RYA CERTIFICATE HERE**

Please note that no record of
certificates is held by the RYA

Enquiries about lost certificates
should be made to the centre
where the course was taken

COURSE CERTIFICATES

**PLEASE ATTACH YOUR
RYA CERTIFICATE HERE**

Please note that no record of
certificates is held by the RYA

Enquiries about lost certificates
should be made to the centre
where the course was taken

COURSE CERTIFICATES

**PLEASE ATTACH YOUR
RYA CERTIFICATE HERE**

Please note that no record of
certificates is held by the RYA

Enquiries about lost certificates
should be made to the centre
where the course was taken

COURSE CERTIFICATES

**PLEASE ATTACH YOUR
RYA CERTIFICATE HERE**

Please note that no record of
certificates is held by the RYA

Enquiries about lost certificates
should be made to the centre
where the course was taken

COURSE CERTIFICATES

**PLEASE ATTACH YOUR
RYA CERTIFICATE HERE**

Please note that no record of
certificates is held by the RYA

Enquiries about lost certificates
should be made to the centre
where the course was taken

COURSE CERTIFICATES

**PLEASE ATTACH YOUR
RYA CERTIFICATE HERE**

Please note that no record of
certificates is held by the RYA

Enquiries about lost certificates
should be made to the centre
where the course was taken